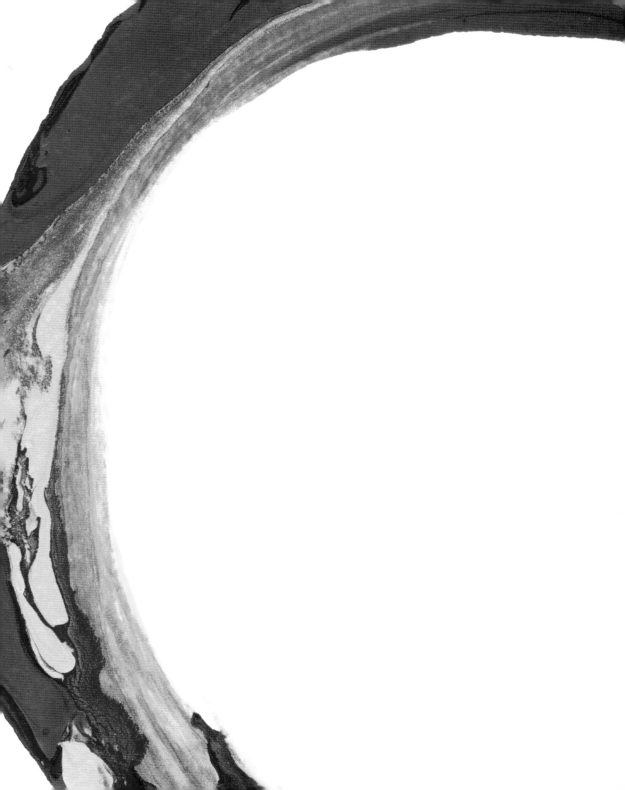

You can't have accuracy
without simplicity.

Each line is complete.

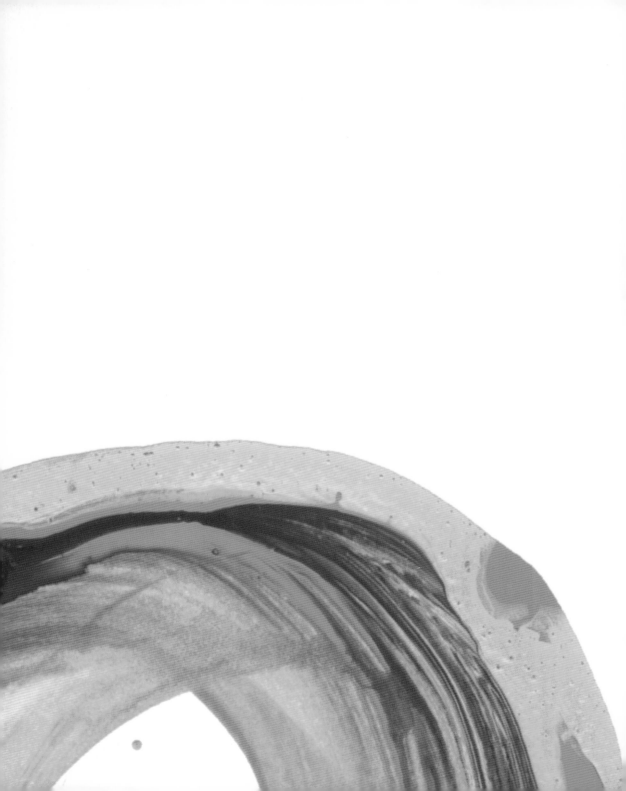

A circle belongs to everyone.
Yet each circle is unique.

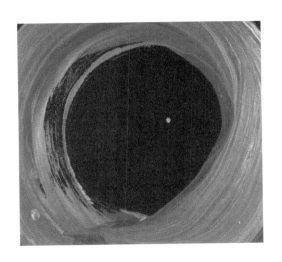

As soon as you accept the acci-
dental effects, they are no longer
accidents. They are a necessity —
the part of yourself that you could
not expect or design beforehand.

Breath is a bridge
between body and mind.

Uniqueness comes from freedom.
Freedom has nothing to do with
attachment or detachment.

The brush was developed to form
organic shapes. When a line is alive,
you always feel the breath of the artist
as well as the breath of the brush.

Less judgement, less trying, less improvement, less regret.

Attentiveness rather than efficiency.
Gentle flow rather than speed.

Every brushstroke must be decisive;
there is no going back. It's just like life.

You can't hide anything in a line.
You are there whatever line you draw.

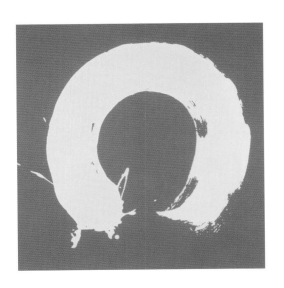

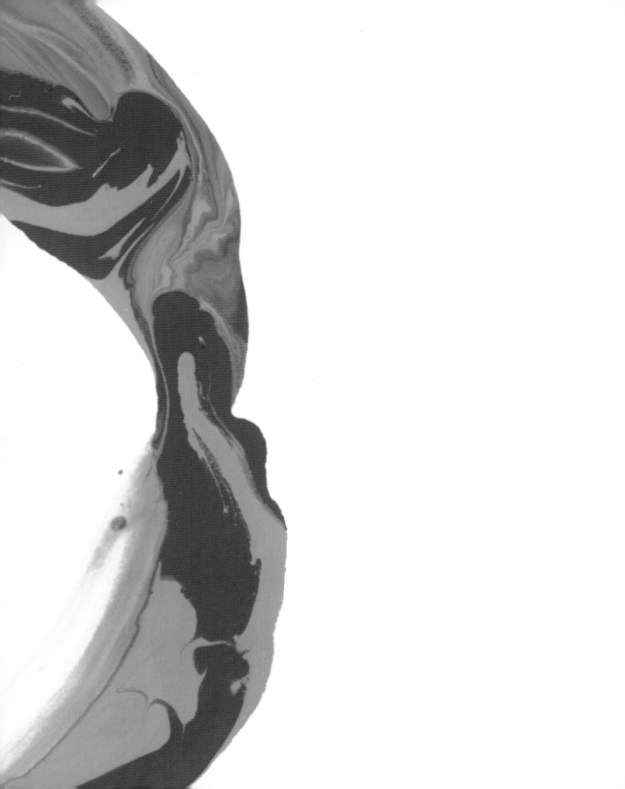

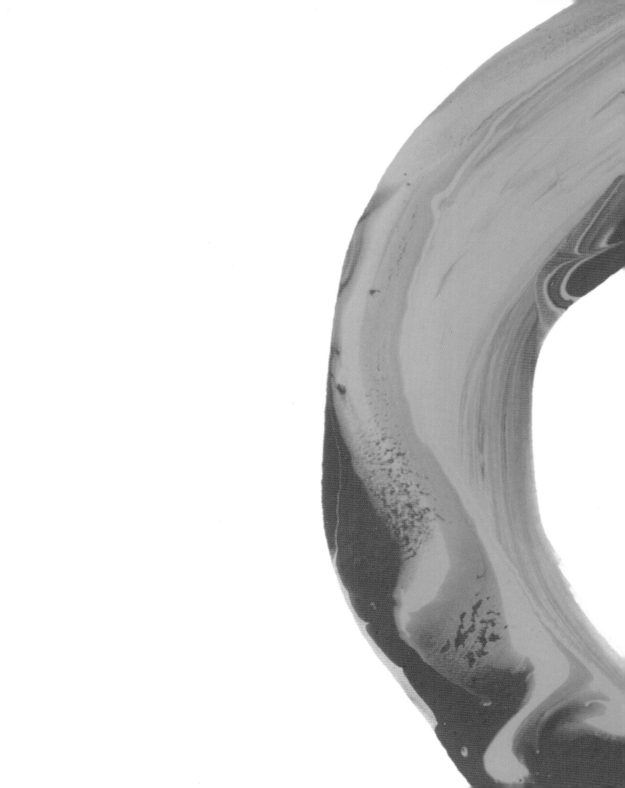

Mind flows.
It is never the same twice.

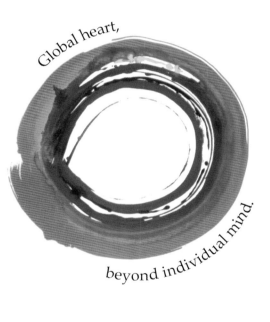

Global heart,

beyond individual mind.

If we learn to enjoy waiting,
we don't have to wait to enjoy.

Masterpieces
may be
one moment away.

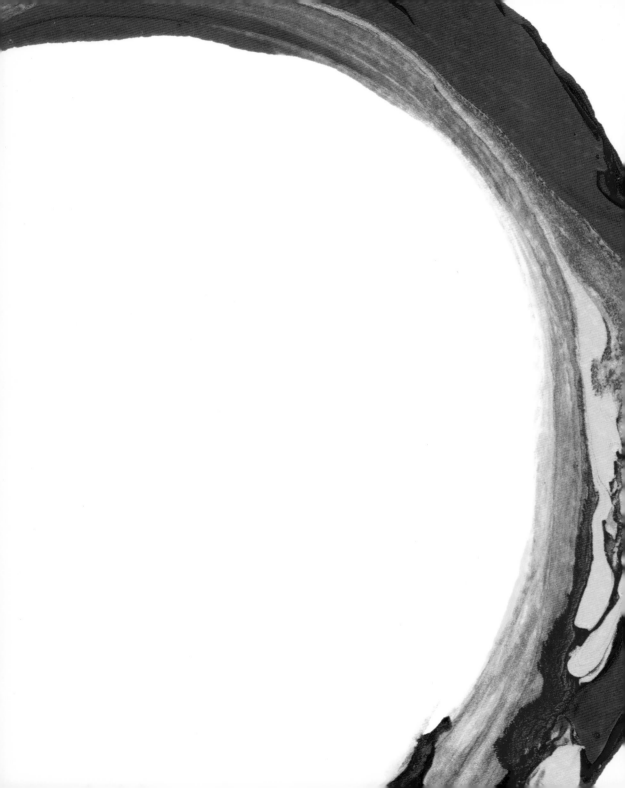

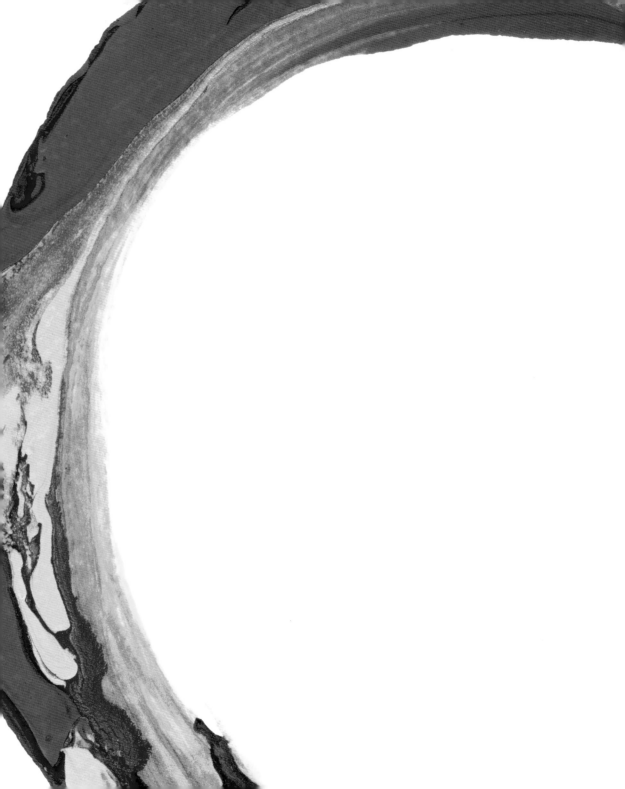

The unpredictable and the
miraculous can be found within.

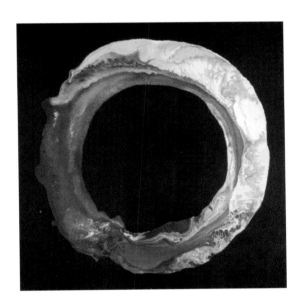

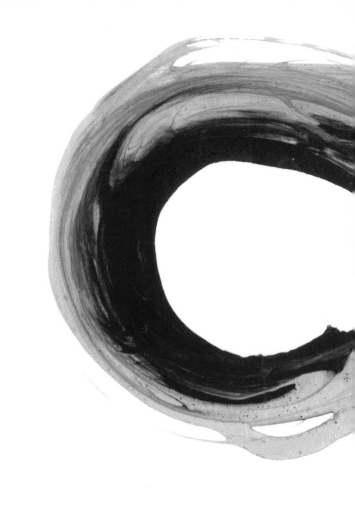

Each moment is a precious expression
of something vast and ungraspable.

Every line we draw carries our wish
for our children and their children.

Brush Dance

Miracles of the Moment

A journal with the circles and words of Kazuaki Tanahashi

While fully in the present, each circle reflects our vision of a world that will sustain the life of future generations. Everything we do, each act, each circle carries our hopes and aspirations. The present and the future awaken together.

For over twenty years, Kazuaki Tanahashi has been creating circle paintings to express the direct experience of living in the moment. Using acrylic paint on paper or canvas, he draws each circle in a single brush stroke, never going back or touching up. Each circle reveals an unpredictable trace of the brush as well as an exquisite interaction of colors. While the artist is in full control of the brush, the outcome is often surprising. The form is as simple as can be, and at the same time very complex.

Some of the words in this journal are reprinted with permission from *Brush Mind*, by Kazuaki Tanahashi, Parallax Press, 1990.

Miracles of the Moment

A journal with the circles and words of Kazuaki Tanahashi

While fully in the present, each circle reflects our vision of a world that will sustain the life of future generations. Everything we do, each act, each circle carries our hopes and aspirations. The present and the future awaken together.

For over twenty years, Kazuaki Tanahashi has been creating circle paintings to express the direct experience of living in the moment. Using acrylic paint on paper or canvas, he draws each circle in a single brush stroke, never going back or touching up. Each circle reveals an unpredictable trace of the brush as well as an exquisite interaction of colors. While the artist is in full control of the brush, the outcome is often surprising. The form is as simple as can be, and at the same time very complex.

Some of the words in this journal are reprinted with permission from Brush Mind, by Kazuaki Tanahashi, Parallax Press, 1990.

 The spiritual path can be seen as the
continuous emergence of one circle after another.

There is no need to think before you paint or write. Your stroke will bring forth the vision.

Each circle is the wholeness
of the moment, inclusive of
the means and the end.

One-stroke painting leaves little
room for thinking; the moment it's
started, it's already done.

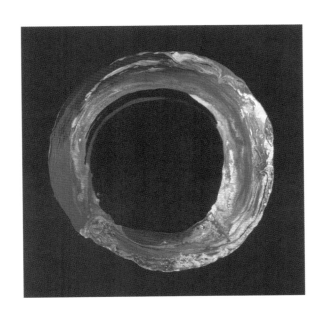

What is obvious is most difficult to see.

Our lives are beyond perspective.

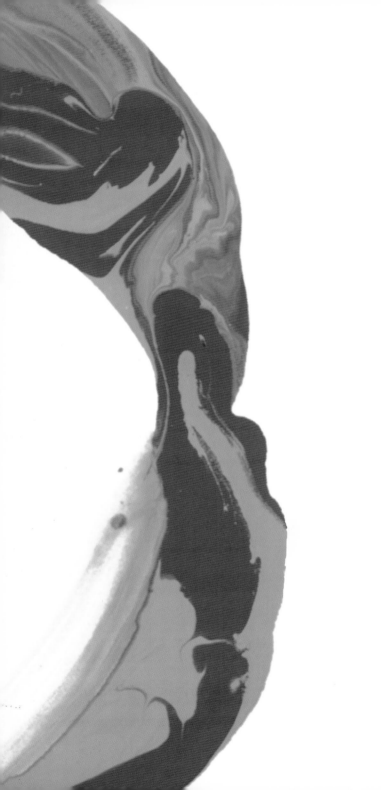

Find a new point of view.

Is there a moon that is not
full? Is there a moment
that is not a miracle?

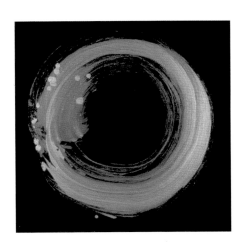

Breakthrough: a sudden and
overwhelming unfolding of
freedom from long held limitations.

If a journey is a departure from where we usually are, a few minutes may be enough for us to go away and come back.

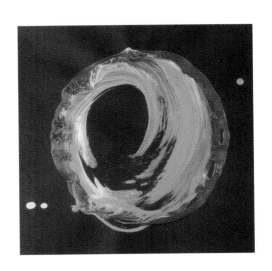

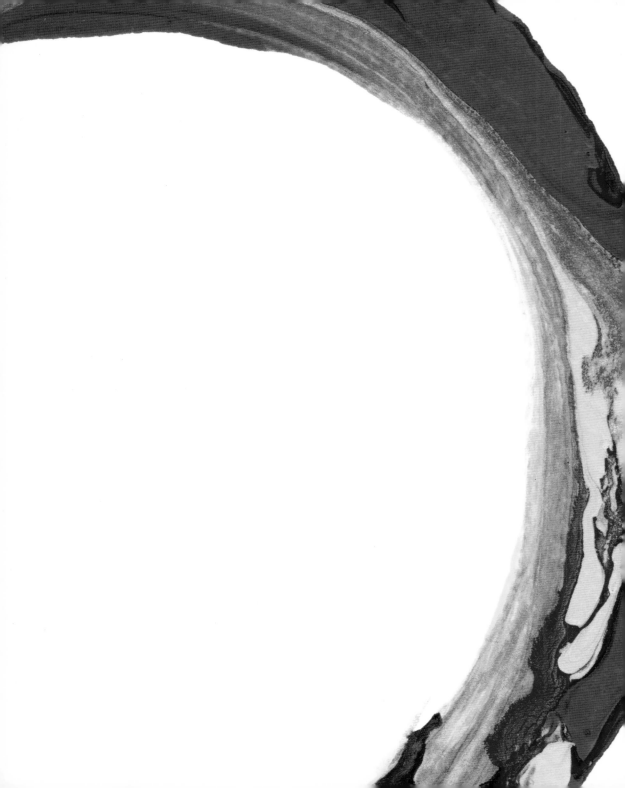